BATTLE FORCE 5™

3

VERT

FACT FILE

FULL NAME: VERT WHEELER

ROLE: BATTLE FORCE 5 LEADER

WEAPONS: DOUBLE-BLADED SWORD;
SPECIAL 'ZOOM' GLASSES

SKILLS: TOP DRIVER,
TACTICAL THINKER, GOOD LEADER

VEHICLE: THE SABER

BFS FACT!
VERT RESCUED THE SENTIENT
SAGE FROM THE VANDALS,
AND WORKS VERY CLOSELY
WITH HER.

THE WHOLE DRIVER'S
COCKPIT ROTATES FOR
A 360-DEGREE VIEW
IN BATTLE.

SPINNING WINGS SHRED ENEMY
CARS UP CLOSE.

BFS FACT!
VERT WAS CHOSEN AS TEAM
LEADER BECAUSE OF HIS
AMAZING DRIVING, GOOD
ATTITUDE AND INSPIRATIONAL
LEADERSHIP SKILLS.

HOT WHEELS
BATTLE 5 FORCE

FIRST PUBLISHED IN THE UK BY HARPERCOLLINS CHILDREN'S BOOKS IN 2011

A CIP CATALOGUE RECORD FOR THIS TITLE IS AVAILABLE FROM THE BRITISH LIBRARY.

WRITTEN BY MATT CROSSICK

WWW.HARPERCOLLINS.CO.UK

PRINTED AND BOUND IN CHINA

BATTLE FORCE 5™

HOW IT ALL BEGAN. . .

FROM RACE DRIVER TO DEFENDER OF THE EARTH IN ONE AFTERNOON!

VERT WHEELER WAS ALREADY A THRILL-
SEEKER BEFORE BATTLE FORCE 5: HE
USED TO SPEED ROUND THE DESERT IN
HIS SOUPED-UP RACE CAR. WHEN HE SAW
A FREAK STORM HEADING HIS WAY ONE
AFTERNOON, THERE WAS ONLY ONE WAY TO
GO: STRAIGHT INTO THE MIDDLE OF IT!

BUT VERT GOT MORE THAN HE BARGAINED
FOR WHEN HE WAS SUCKED UP AND SPAT
OUT IN ANOTHER WORLD — A STRANGE, BLEAK
WORLD FULL OF FIERCE MONSTERS AND
KILLER ROBOTS.

WHEN HE SEES A GROUP OF ROBOTS
ATTACKING A HELPLESS ALIEN, HE HAS TO
INTERVENE — AND USES HIS AMAZING DRIVING
SKILLS TO SCATTER THE ROBOTS AND BRING
SAGE BACK TO EARTH WITH HIM. SHE
EXPLAINS ALL ABOUT THE MULTIVERSE,
STORMSHOCKS AND HOW THE WORLD
COULD BE DESTROYED BY VANDALS
AND THE SARK.

VERT ISN'T GOING TO SIT BACK AND LET
THE EARTH BE DESTROYED, THOUGH. SAGE
SETS HIM UP WITH A SENTIENT TECHNOLOGY
CAR, A COOL RACE SUIT AND A HI-TECH
UNDERGROUND BASE BELOW HIS GARAGE.

ALL HE NEEDS NOW IS SOME ACTION,
AND WHEN A STORMSHOCK OPENS UP
NEARBY, VERT IS SENT ON HIS FIRST
MISSION. FROM EXPERT DRIVER TO
SAVIOUR OF THE WORLD... NOT BAD
FOR AN AFTERNOON'S WORK!

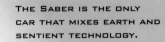

THE SABER IS THE ONLY CAR THAT MIXES EARTH AND SENTIENT TECHNOLOGY.

BFS FACT!
VERT IS DESCRIBED AS 'THE ONE WITH FIRE IN HIS SPIRIT' IN SENTIENT LEGENDS.

THE WHOLE FRONT END TURNS INTO A FEARSOME BLADE WEAPON, BY TWISTING THE WHEELS SIDEWAYS!

THE SABER

THE SABER IS SO STRONG IT CAN HOLD ANOTHER VEHICLE WITHOUT BEING CRUSHED.

THE LONG, SHARP SWORD SHAPE MEANS VERT CAN CHOP HIS RIVALS APART ON THE ROAD!

··· INCREDIBLE SPEED MAKES THE SABER THE FIRST CAR INTO BATTLE.

BFS FACT!
HIS RED RACING SUIT WAS ALSO CREATED BY SAGE AND MATCHES THE SABER.

BFS FACT!
DESPITE BATTLING MONSTERS REGULARLY, VERT ONLY HAS ONE EARTH-BASED ENEMY – SHERIFF JOHNSON, WHO IS ALWAYS TRYING TO CATCH VERT SPEEDING!

BATTLE ZONES

WHAT ARE BATTLE ZONES?

BATTLE ZONES ARE INTER-DIMENSIONAL WORLDS CREATED A LONG TIME AGO BY THE SENTIENTS. THEY ARE BARREN, EMPTY LANDS SUITABLE FOR FIGHTING AND NOT MUCH ELSE – BUT BECAUSE THEY CAN BE ACCESSED BY VANDALS, THE SARK AND ALSO PEOPLE ON EARTH, THE FATE OF THE WORLD DEPENDS ON THEM!

HOW DO YOU REACH THEM?

Through a Stormshock. These twisting hurricane-like portals between dimensions open up and allow humans, The Sark and Vandals to enter Battle Zones. BF5 enter Battle Zones by driving their tough vehicles into Stormshocks at high speed.

WHY ARE THEY DANGEROUS?

Because they allow The Sark and Vandals access to Earth. These war-like warriors and monsters are desperate to invade Earth, like they have invaded and destroyed the Sentient worlds. It's up to Battle Force 5 to lock the Battle Zones down before the enemy can get through to our planet!

HOW CAN THE TEAM MAKE THEM SAFE?

By locking each Battle Zone down with a Battle Key. The team need to find the Battle Key in each zone, and take it out of the zone back to Earth to safely lock that Battle Zone down: after that, no Vandals or Sark can come through to our planet.

SOME MAJOR BATTLE ZONES

Each Battle Zone has its own strange characteristics. Here are a few of the best ones:

- City Wreck Battle Zone
- Lava Battle Zone
- Squid Battle Zone
- Maze Battle Zone
- Storm Battle Zone
- Coliseum Battle Zone
- Spider Web Battle Zone

THE TEAM IS BORN

BECAUSE VERT CAN'T DO IT ALONE!

VERT WHEELER WORKS ALONE. OR SO HE SAYS! BUT THAT'S BEFORE HE FINDS HIMSELF SURROUNDED BY ZEMERIK AND OTHER SARK IN A GRIM BATTLE ZONE. LOOKING ACROSS AT THE METAL ARMY ON WHEELS, IT DAWNS ON VERT THAT SOME RECON EXPERIENCE MIGHT BE HANDY. OH, AND SOME MUSCLE TO CRUSH A FEW ROBOTS. AND SOMEONE WHO COULD ATTACK FROM A DISTANCE TOO, FOR THAT MATTER. . .

AS VERT FLEES THROUGH THE PORTAL, THE SARK FLY THROUGH AFTER HIM. BUT UNKNOWN TO VERT, SAGE HAS BEEN BUSY, AND A BRAND NEW TEAM IS WAITING ON THE OTHER SIDE FOR HIM.

BEFORE THEY HAVE EVEN BEEN INTRODUCED, THEY ARE FACING AN ANGRY ROBOT MOB! ZOOM SPRINGS INTO THE AIR WITH A KUNG-FU ATTACK, SHERMAN AND SPINNER BASH SOME METAL HEADS TOGETHER AND AGURA RIPS A ZURK HEAD CLEAN OFF ITS SHOULDERS.

STANFORD, OF COURSE, STILL COMPLAINS THAT HE WAS PROMISED A PARTY. IN FACT, THEY WERE ALL TRICKED INTO COMING TO THE DESERT – AGURA THOUGHT SHE WAS ENTERING AN OFF-ROAD RACE, AND SPINNER WAS COMING TO A VIDEO GAMES CHAMPIONSHIP.

BUT AFTER SAGE WARNS THEM ALL OF THE DANGER EARTH IS IN, THERE'S NO QUESTION OF VERT GOING IT ALONE ANY MORE. THE TEAM ARE GIVEN SHOCKSUITS OF THEIR OWN, SOME SERIOUSLY COOL WHEELS, AND A NEW NAME: BATTLE FORCE 5 – SO CALLED BECAUSE THEY HAVE 5 AWESOME VEHICLES.

BATTLE FORCE 5™

STANFORD

FACT FILE

FULL NAME: STANFORD ISAAC RHODES IV
ROLE: BF5 WEAPONS EXPERT
WEAPONS: DEAFENING SONIC BLAST THAT
           CAN KNOCK OUT OPPONENTS
           FROM LONG RANGE
SKILLS: ACOUSTICAL EXPERT, CAN MAP
           BATTLE ZONES AND FIND KEYS
           WITH HIS HI-TECH SONIC
           EQUIPMENT.
VEHICLE: THE REVERB

BATTLE FORCE 5 PROFILE

BF5 FACT!
STANFORD CLAIMS HE IS
DESCENDED FROM ROYALTY –
HE IS 188TH IN LINE TO THE
BRITISH THRONE!

THE REVERB'S SONIC
SYSTEM CAN ALSO ECHO-
MAP BATTLE ZONES FOR
THE TEAM.

ECHO-MAPS CAN FIND ENEMY
HIDEOUTS AND LOST BATTLE
KEYS TOO.

BF5 FACT!
STANFORD LOVES MUSIC AS
MUCH AS HE LOVES CARS,
AND IS ALWAYS THE FIRST
TEAM MEMBER TO SUGGEST
A PARTY.

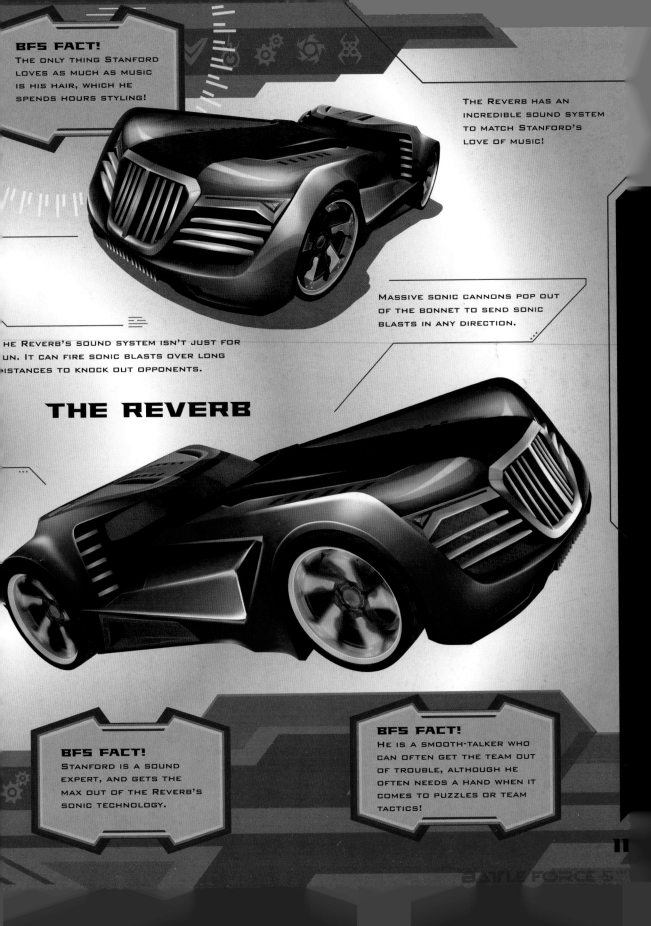

THE REVERB HAS AN
INCREDIBLE SOUND SYSTEM
TO MATCH STANFORD'S
LOVE OF MUSIC!

MASSIVE SONIC CANNONS POP OUT
OF THE BONNET TO SEND SONIC
BLASTS IN ANY DIRECTION.

HE REVERB'S SOUND SYSTEM ISN'T JUST FOR
UN. IT CAN FIRE SONIC BLASTS OVER LONG
ISTANCES TO KNOCK OUT OPPONENTS.

THE REVERB

BATTLE FORCE 5

ZOOM

FACT FILE

FULL NAME: ZOOM TAKAZUMI
ROLE: BF5 TEAM SCOUT
WEAPONS: MARTIAL ARTS SKILLS;
                    SPINNING BLADES ON CHOPPER
SKILLS: AGILE, QUIET, VERY GOOD AT
                    STEALTH OPERATIONS AND
                    HAND-TO-HAND FIGHTING.
VEHICLE: THE CHOPPER

BF5 FACT!
ZOOM IS THE YOUNGEST
MEMBER OF BATTLE FORCE 5,
ALTHOUGH HE HATES BEING
CALLED A KID!

IN ZOOM'S HANDS,
THE CHOPPER IS THE
MOST AGILE VEHICLE ON
THE TEAM AND CAN BE
USED TO SQUEEZE INTO
SMALLER SPACES THAN
THE OTHER CARS!

THE CHOPPER IS
FAST AND QUIET,
PERFECT FOR THE
BF5 TEAM SCOUT!

BF5 FACT!
ZOOM HAS AMAZING MARTIAL
ARTS SKILLS AND IS VERY
FAST AND ATHLETIC.

BF5 FACT!

ZOOM LOOKS UP TO VERT AND IS THE FIRST TO OFFER HIM HELP WHEN HE NEEDS IT.

THE CHOPPER'S WHEELS CAN SPLIT IN TWO, TO MAKE THE MOTORBIKE HOVER IN THE AIR FOR SHORT PERIODS.

A CABLE CAN SHOOT OUT OF THE CHOPPER TO LATCH ONTO OTHER BF5 VEHICLES. ZOOM CAN USE THIS CABLE TO FLING HIMSELF INTO THE AIR FOR SHORT PERIODS.

THE CHOPPER

THE CHOPPER'S SPLIT WHEELS CAN ALSO BE USED AS SPINNING BLADE WEAPONS IN BATTLE.

BF5 FACT!

HE USED TO BELONG TO THE ORDER OF THE FLYING FIST, AN ELITE MARTIAL ARTS SCHOOL, BACK HOME IN BANGKOK.

BF5 FACT!

WHEN NOT OUT ON A MISSION, ZOOM IS RESTLESS AND GETS BORED VERY EASILY!

13

AGURA

FACT FILE

FULL NAME: AGURA IBADEN
ROLE: BF5 FIRST LIEUTENANT
WEAPONS: GRAPPLING HOOKS AND ROBOT
'ARMS' ON THE TANGLER
SKILLS: QUICK, BRAVE, SKILLED HUNTER
AND TRAPPER.
VEHICLE: THE TANGLER ATV

BF5 FACT!
AGURA IS THE ONLY GIRL ON
THE BF5 TEAM, BUT WON'T
LET ANYONE SUGGEST SHE
IS WEAKER THAN THE BOYS.

THE TANGLER IS AN ALL-
TERRAIN VEHICLE WITH
TELESCOPIC LIMBS, WHICH
ALLOW IT TO 'WALK' OVER
TOUGH GROUND.

IT CAN FIRE CABLES
TO SNARE ENEMIES
OR TO DRAG OTHER
VEHICLES ALONG.

BF5 FACT!
STANFORD ISN'T THE ONLY
TEAM MEMBER WITH ROYAL
BLOOD. AGURA IS AN
AFRICAN PRINCESS!

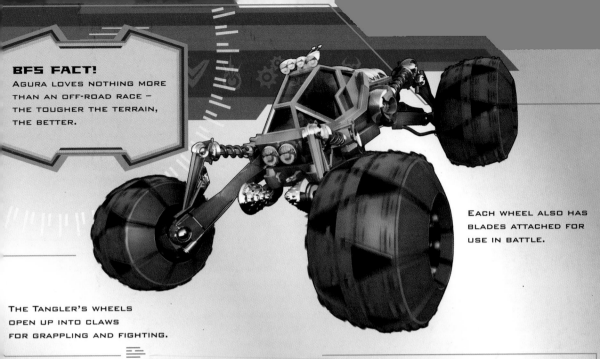

BFS FACT!
AGURA LOVES NOTHING MORE THAN AN OFF-ROAD RACE – THE TOUGHER THE TERRAIN, THE BETTER.

EACH WHEEL ALSO HAS BLADES ATTACHED FOR USE IN BATTLE.

THE TANGLER'S WHEELS OPEN UP INTO CLAWS FOR GRAPPLING AND FIGHTING.

THE TANGLER ATV

THE TANGLER IS UNSTOPPABLE WHEN TRACKING DOWN AN ENEMY, ESPECIALLY WITH SKILLED HUNTER AGURA AT THE WHEEL!

BFS FACT!
HER HUNTING SKILLS ARE ESSENTIAL TO THE TEAM WHEN TRACKING DOWN ENEMIES.

BFS FACT!
AGURA IS SECOND-IN-COMMAND OF BATTLE FORCE 5, AND THE BOSS WHEN VERT ISN'T AROUND.

BATTLE FORCE 5 PROFILE

SHERMAN & SPINNER

FACT FILE

FULL NAME: SHERMAN AND SPINNER CORTEZ
ROLE: BF5 TECHNICAL SUPPORT TEAM
WEAPONS: A WHOLE ARMY'S WORTH ON THE BUSTER
SKILLS: SHERMAN: STRONG, MECHANICAL GENIUS. SPINNER: VIDEO GAME CHAMP, PRACTICAL JOKER.
VEHICLE: THE BUSTER TANK

SUPER-TOUGH BODY ARMOUR MAKES THE BUSTER NEARLY INVINCIBLE.

BF5 FACT!
SHERMAN IS HUGE, STRONG AND VERY GOOD AT MATHS, BUT HE IS SHY AROUND NEW PEOPLE.

BATTLE SPIKES PROJECT FROM THE SIDES TO SMASH ENEMY VEHICLES.

BF5 FACT!
SHERMAN IS A MECHANICAL GENIUS AND IS A KEY TACTICAL PART OF THE BF5 TEAM.

A RAMP CAN
LAUNCH OR
RESCUE OTHER
BF5 VEHICLES
IN DANGEROUS
SITUATIONS.

THE BUSTER IS
BUILT FOR RAMMING
AND CAN SMASH
ENEMY CARS OR
EVEN BASES TO
SMITHEREENS
– ESPECIALLY
WHEN COMBINED
WITH THE TANK'S
AFTERBURNERS!

THE BUSTER TANK

THE BUSTER HAS A ROTATING
TURRET THAT CAN FIRE ON
ENEMIES IN BATTLE.

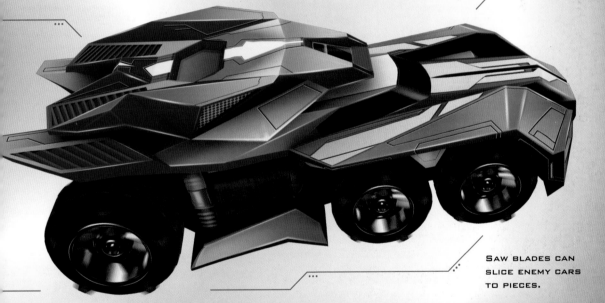

SAW BLADES CAN
SLICE ENEMY CARS
TO PIECES.

BATTLE FORCE 5™

BATTLE 5 FORCE

THE SARK

THE SARK ARE A RACE OF SUPER-ROBOTS, WHO LIVE BY INVADING AND DESTROYING OTHER PLANETS. THEY ARE COLD, CALCULATING AND RUTHLESS.

THE SARK ARE SUPER-LOGICAL AND PROGRAMMED TO DESTROY ORGANIC LIFE. THEY HAVE NO EMOTIONS, AND NO FEELINGS: THEY JUST KNOW HOW TO DO ONE THING — FIGHT AND WIN!

THE SARK INVADED ONE OF THE TWIN SENTIENT PLANETS, AND NOW THEY HAVE THEIR SIGHTS SET ON EARTH TOO.

SARK VEHICLES ARE SUPER HI-TEC MACHINES THAT CAN TRANSFORM, SHRED RIVAL CARS AND TRAVEL AT BLISTERING SPEED. IN SARK HANDS, THEY ARE DEADLY WEAPONS!

NOT EVERYONE LOVES BATTLE FORCE 5! THESE MONSTERS ARE DESPERATE TO DESTROY BATTLE FORCE 5 AND INVADE EARTH...

THE VANDALS

THE VANDALS ARE A RACE OF EXTREME HUNTER WARRIORS, WITH ANIMAL-LIKE FEATURES AND A BLOODTHIRSTY NATURE. THEY ARE FIERCE, TOUGH AND USUALLY ANGRY!

THE VANDALS INVADED THE SECOND SENTIENT PLANET, AND LIKE THE SARK THEY SEE EARTH AS THEIR NEXT CONQUEST.

VANDAL VEHICLES LOOK LIKE THEIR OWNERS. THEY AREN'T HI-TECH OR COMPUTERIZED – THEY ARE BRUTAL AND SAVAGE. THEY CAN SPEAR, CRUNCH OR SMASH RIVAL CARS INTO SMITHEREENS.

THE VANDALS AND THE SARK ARE NO FRIENDS TO EACH OTHER. THEY BOTH WANT EARTH, AND THEY DON'T MIND FIGHTING EACH OTHER FOR IT, AS WELL AS BATTLE FORCE 5!

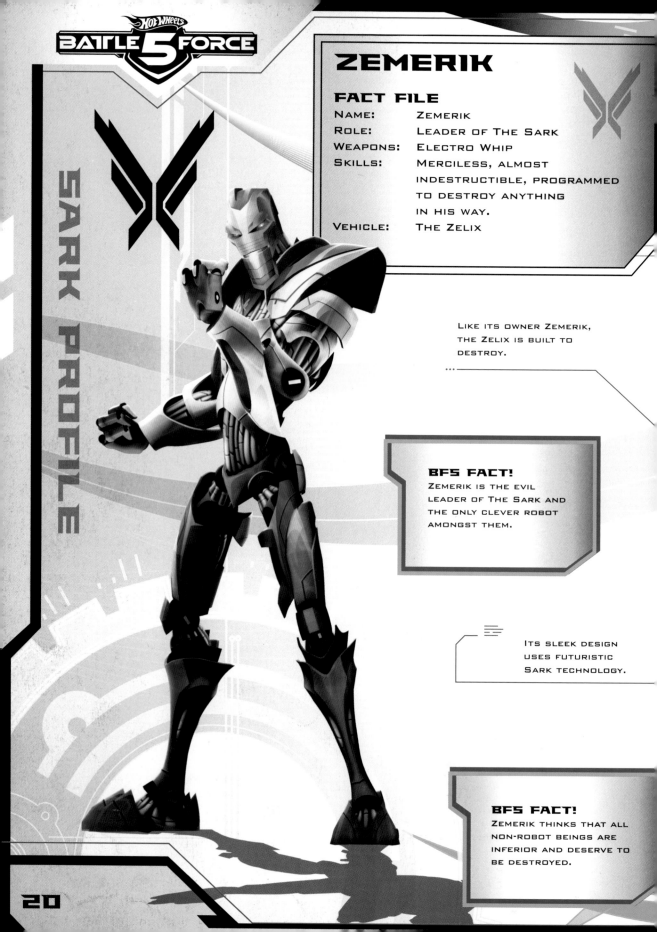

SARK PROFILE

ZEMERIK

FACT FILE
NAME: ZEMERIK
ROLE: LEADER OF THE SARK
WEAPONS: ELECTRO WHIP
SKILLS: MERCILESS, ALMOST
INDESTRUCTIBLE, PROGRAMMED
TO DESTROY ANYTHING
IN HIS WAY.
VEHICLE: THE ZELIX

LIKE ITS OWNER ZEMERIK, THE ZELIX IS BUILT TO DESTROY.

BF5 FACT!
ZEMERIK IS THE EVIL LEADER OF THE SARK AND THE ONLY CLEVER ROBOT AMONGST THEM.

ITS SLEEK DESIGN USES FUTURISTIC SARK TECHNOLOGY.

BF5 FACT!
ZEMERIK THINKS THAT ALL NON-ROBOT BEINGS ARE INFERIOR AND DESERVE TO BE DESTROYED.

DARK MATTER
ENERGY BLADES
SHRED ANY VEHICLES
IN ITS PATH.

THE ZELIX

THE ZELIX HAS ITS OWN
ELECTRO-WHIP TO TAKE OUT
ENEMIES IN BATTLE.

BATTLE FORCE 5™

SARK PROFILE

ZUG

FACT FILE
NAME: ZUG
ROLE: SARK SECOND-IN-COMMAND
WEAPONS: MASSIVE STRENGTH
SKILLS: ZURK IS ZEMERIK'S MUSCLE. HE IS STRONG, VIOLENT, AND DOESN'T THINK TOO MUCH.
VEHICLE: THE ZENDRILL

BFS FACT!
ZUG'S PROGRAMMING IS SIMPLE: DO WHAT ZEMERIK TELLS HIM TO!

DARK MATTER BLADES MAKE THE ZENDRILL EVEN MORE DEADLY.

THE ZENDRILL IS MADE UP OF A MASSIVE DRILL, FOR TUNNELING THROUGH ROCK. . . OR ANY VEHICLES IN HIS PATH!

BFS FACT!
ZUG MAKES UP FOR HIS LACK OF INTELLIGENCE WITH HIS HUGE STRENGTH.

BFS FACT!
LIKE THE OTHER SARK, ZUG ONLY KNOWS HOW TO KILL AND DESTROY. IT IS WHAT HE WAS PROGRAMMED FOR.

LIKE ITS OWNER, THE ZENDRILL IS SIMPLE BUT STRONG!

THE ZENDRILL

THE ZURK

FACT FILE

NAME: THE ZURK
ROLE: SARK FOOT SOLDIERS
WEAPONS: DARK MATTER SPIKES
SKILLS: SWARMING ENEMIES, DESTRUCTION.
VEHICLE: ZENTNERS

BFS FACT!
ZURKS HAVE NO FREE WILL, AND ONLY DO WHAT ZEMERIK TELLS THEM TO DO.

ZENTNERS

BFS FACT!
ZURKS ARE DANGEROUS WHEN THEY SWARM ENEMIES IN GREAT NUMBERS.

ZENTNERS ARE ALL THE SAME, LIKE THE ZURK WHO RIDE THEM.

BIG DARK MATTER SPINES MAKE THESE ROBOT MACHINES DEADLY.

ZENTNERS WORK WELL WHEN DRIVEN AT ENEMIES IN PACKS.

BFS FACT!
ZEMERIK TREATS ZURKS AS DISPOSABLE WARRIORS, AND DOESN'T CARE WHEN THEY GET DESTROYED IN BATTLE WITH BATTLE FORCE 5.

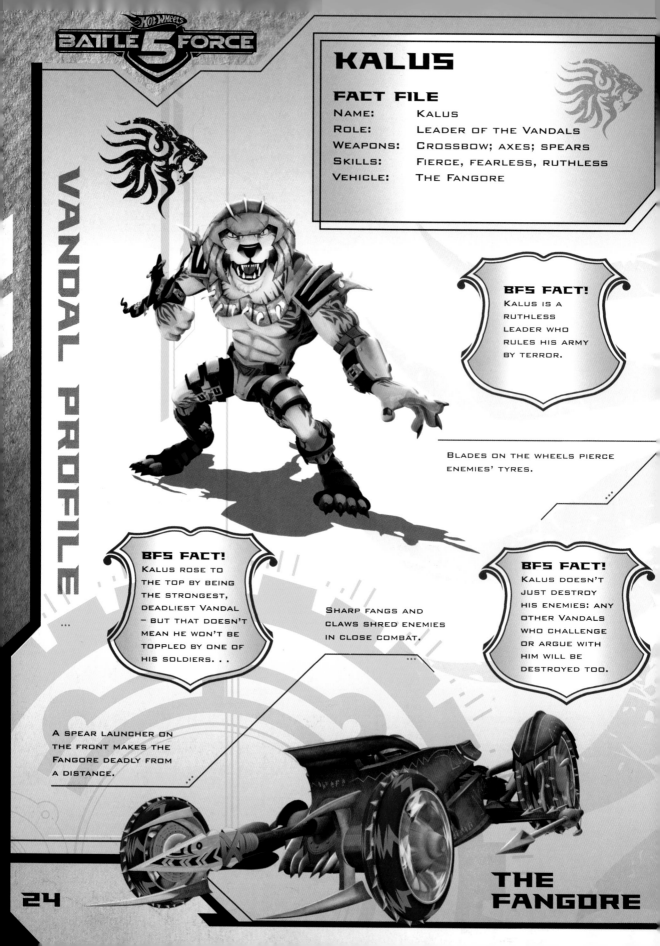

BATTLE 5 FORCE

VANDAL PROFILE

KALUS

FACT FILE

NAME: KALUS
ROLE: LEADER OF THE VANDALS
WEAPONS: CROSSBOW; AXES; SPEARS
SKILLS: FIERCE, FEARLESS, RUTHLESS
VEHICLE: THE FANGORE

BFS FACT!
KALUS IS A RUTHLESS LEADER WHO RULES HIS ARMY BY TERROR.

BLADES ON THE WHEELS PIERCE ENEMIES' TYRES.

BFS FACT!
KALUS ROSE TO THE TOP BY BEING THE STRONGEST, DEADLIEST VANDAL – BUT THAT DOESN'T MEAN HE WON'T BE TOPPLED BY ONE OF HIS SOLDIERS. . .

SHARP FANGS AND CLAWS SHRED ENEMIES IN CLOSE COMBAT.

BFS FACT!
KALUS DOESN'T JUST DESTROY HIS ENEMIES: ANY OTHER VANDALS WHO CHALLENGE OR ARGUE WITH HIM WILL BE DESTROYED TOO.

A SPEAR LAUNCHER ON THE FRONT MAKES THE FANGORE DEADLY FROM A DISTANCE.

THE FANGORE

KROCOMODO

FACT FILE

NAME:	KROCOMODO
ROLE:	VANDALS SECOND-IN-COMMAND
WEAPONS:	KILLER JAWS
SKILLS:	SLY, SNEAKY, RUTHLESS
VEHICLE:	THE RIPTILE

BFS FACT!
KROCOMODO IS NO LOYAL SECOND-IN-COMMAND. HE PLANS TO OVERTHROW KALUS AND RULE THE VANDALS HIMSELF.

THE RIPTILE IS AN ARMOURED ALL-TERRAIN BUGGY WITH DEADLY WEAPONS.

THE RIPTILE

BFS FACT!
HE IS AN EXPERT AT SECRET, SLY TRICKS AND PLAYING PEOPLE OFF AGAINST EACH OTHER.

STRONG JAWS CAN CLAMP RIVAL CARS BEFORE DESTROYING THEM.

SPRING-LOADED WEAPONS CAN BITE THROUGH ENEMIES.

BFS FACT!
HIS MASSIVE JAWS ARE DEADLY UP CLOSE!

HATCH

FACT FILE

NAME:	HATCH
ROLE:	VANDAL WARRIOR
WEAPONS:	MAGICAL AURA MAKES HIM INVISIBLE TO INSECTS
SKILLS:	SOME MAGICAL POWERS, EXPERT IN ELECTRONICS.
VEHICLE:	THE SCARIB

VANDAL PROFILE

BFS FACT!
HATCH IS THE VANDALS' ELECTRONICS EXPERT, ALTHOUGH HIS CREATIONS AREN'T VERY HIGH-TECH COMPARED TO SAGE'S TECHNOLOGICAL WIZARDRY!

BFS FACT!
HATCH, UNLIKE KROCOMODO, IS COWARDLY AND SHY, AND HAS NO DESIRE TO TAKE OVER LEADERSHIP OF THE VANDALS. THAT DOESN'T MEAN HE ISN'T CUNNING, THOUGH. . .

A VICIOUS TAIL STINGER INJECTS POISON INTO ENEMIES.

THE SCARIB IS A BONE-SHAKING, SPIKY CAR THAT LOOKS A LOT LIKE ITS DRIVER!

BFS FACT!
HE HAS SOME MAGIC SKILLS THAT HE CAN USE WHEN UNDER ATTACK, INCLUDING MAKING HIMSELF INVISIBLE TO INSECTS.

THE SCARIB

GRAPPLING HOOKS LE[T] HATCH GRAB HOLD OF ENEMIES BEFORE STINGING THEM.

BFS FACT!

SEVER USES HIS KEEN SENSE OF SMELL TO SNIFF OUT BATTLE FORCE 5 WHEN THEY ARE IN BATTLE ZONES.

SEVER

FACT FILE

NAME: SEVER
ROLE: VANDAL WARRIOR
WEAPONS: LONG TEETH AND STRONG JAWS.
SKILLS: AMAZING SENSE OF SMELL, LOYAL TO KALUS.
VEHICLE: THE WATER SLAUGHTER

THE WATER SLAUGHTER CAN EVEN FIRE TOOTH BULLETS TO STOP RIVALS IN THEIR TRACKS.

BFS FACT!

HE IS A FIERCE WARRIOR WHO THINKS NOTHING OF KILLING HIS ENEMIES WITH HIS SHARP TEETH.

THE WATER SLAUGHTER HAS SPINNING, RAZOR-SHARP TEETH THAT CAN CHEW AND SHRED ENEMY CARS.

THE WATER SLAUGHTER

CLAMPING JAWS CAN NEUTRALIZE OTHER CARS WITH A VICE-LIKE GRIP.

BFS FACT!

SEVER IS ONE OF THE ONLY VANDALS WHO HASN'T OPENLY TRIED TO REBEL AGAINST KALUS.

27

GOING INTO BATTLE

HOW DO BATTLE FORCE 5 FACE
UP TO THEIR DEADLY ENEMIES?

SPINNER AND SHERMAN USUALLY BRING UP THE REAR, PROVIDING
SUPPORT AND BRINGING SOME NECESSARY MUSCLE INTO THE FIGHT.
THEY CAN HOLD A TEAM OF SARK OR VANDALS AT BAY WITH EASE,
ALLOWING THE REST OF THE TEAM TO GET ON WITH THE JOB!

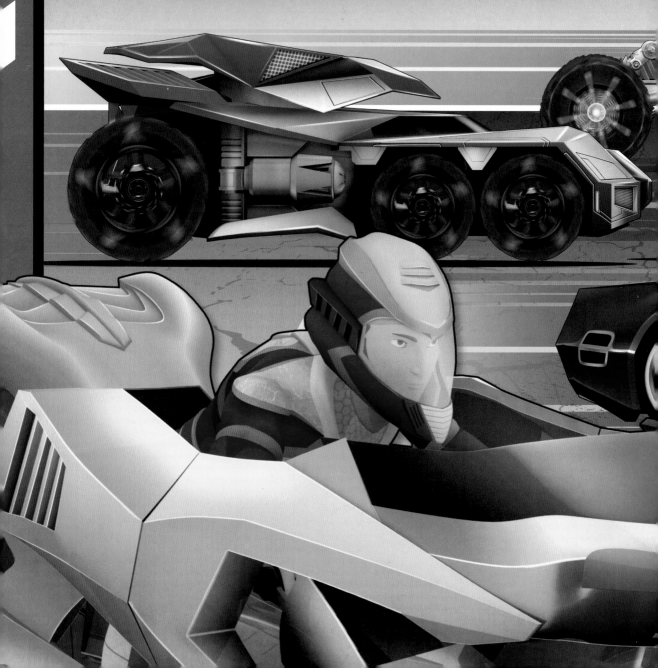

AGURA IS A KEY FIGHTER THANKS TO HER ROUGH ALL-TERRAIN CAR. SHE IS THE TEAM HUNTER, AND IS GOOD AT CHASING DOWN AND CATCHING ANY ENEMIES WHO SNARE THE BATTLE KEY OR ONE OF HER TEAM-MATES.

VERT LEADS THE WAY AND COMES UP WITH THE BATTLE PLAN. HE GIVES EACH TEAM MEMBER A JOB TO DO, AND IS ALWAYS THE FIRST CAR INTO — AND OUT OF — THE STORMSHOCK.

STANFORD IS VERY HANDY IN A FIGHT THANKS TO HIS LONG-RANGE SONIC BLASTS, THAT CAN KNOCK AN ENEMY CAR OUT FROM A DISTANCE. PLUS, HIS 'SONIC MAPS' CAN REVEAL HIDDEN ENEMIES AS WELL AS THE LAY OF THE LAND IN ANY NEW BATTLE ZONE.

ZOOM IS FAST AND NIMBLE, SO HE IS USUALLY DISPATCHED TO FIND THE BATTLE KEY IN THE NEW BATTLE ZONE, WHILE THE OTHERS TAKE CARE OF THE ENEMY. HE CAN SPEED PAST ANY RIVALS AND JUMP THROUGH THE AIR TO SECURE THE KEY BEFORE ANY VANDALS OR SARK MAKE IT THERE FIRST.

BATTLE MODE

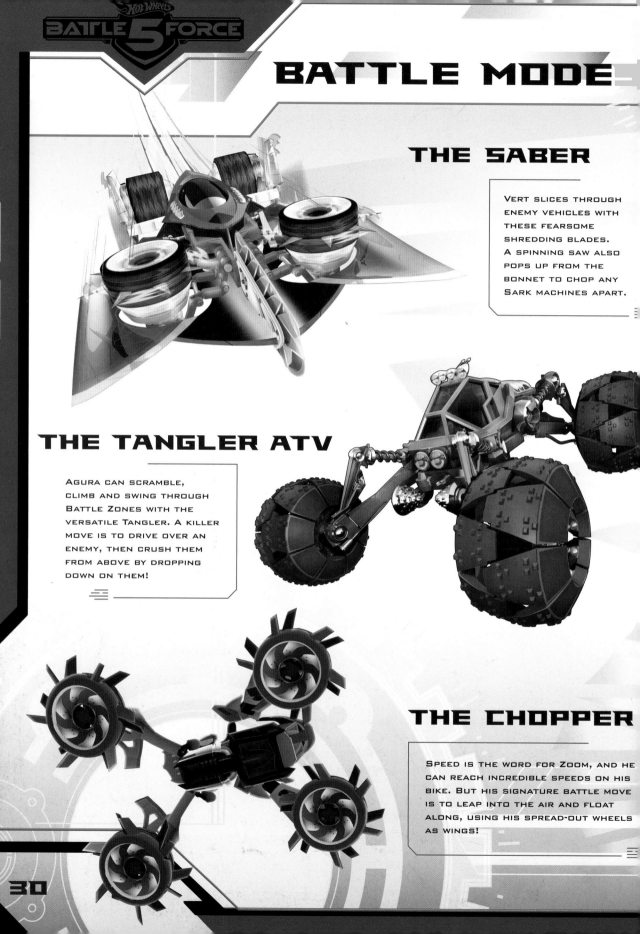

THE SABER

VERT SLICES THROUGH ENEMY VEHICLES WITH THESE FEARSOME SHREDDING BLADES. A SPINNING SAW ALSO POPS UP FROM THE BONNET TO CHOP ANY SARK MACHINES APART.

THE TANGLER ATV

AGURA CAN SCRAMBLE, CLIMB AND SWING THROUGH BATTLE ZONES WITH THE VERSATILE TANGLER. A KILLER MOVE IS TO DRIVE OVER AN ENEMY, THEN CRUSH THEM FROM ABOVE BY DROPPING DOWN ON THEM!

THE CHOPPER

SPEED IS THE WORD FOR ZOOM, AND HE CAN REACH INCREDIBLE SPEEDS ON HIS BIKE. BUT HIS SIGNATURE BATTLE MOVE IS TO LEAP INTO THE AIR AND FLOAT ALONG, USING HIS SPREAD-OUT WHEELS AS WINGS!

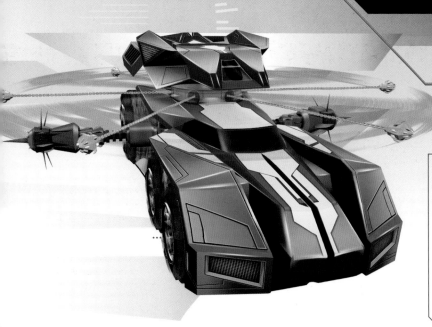

THE BUSTER TANK

Sherman and Spinner have an army's worth of weapons to hand in the Buster Tank. These spinning spikes and spears that shoot out from the sides are the deadliest, and can smash a Vandal car or Sark machine clean off the road.

THE REVERB

These two sonic guns fire devastating sonic blasts over long distances. They can knock a car clean off the road, while the Reverb's on-board computer can use the sound-waves they produce to map a Battle Zone.

VEHICLE DESIGN

The Battle Force 5 vehicles aren't built using human skills: they use advanced Sentient technology to produce their incredible features. This means that they can change shape at the touch of a button, fuse together in exciting ways, and of course travel at incredible speeds. Sage created them especially for each team member, and they are driven by Hadron energy. They can only be repaired in the Hub, or in the Mobias Command Centre. Only Vert has any earth technology in his vehicle – as his original car was transformed by Sage in the first episode.

STORMSHOCKS

WHAT ARE STORMSHOCKS?

Stormshocks are twisting tornadoes that act as portals to Battle Zones from other planets in the Multiverse. To cross the portal and enter the Battle Zone, cars have to drive into the eye of the storm, and up the inside of the tornado.

WHERE DO STORMSHOCKS LEAD?

They lead to Battle Zones – inter-dimensional worlds created purely for the purpose of doing battle. Before entering a Stormshock, the team have no idea which Battle Zone it will lead to – or who will be waiting for them on the other side!

WHERE CAN THEY BE FOUND?

Stormshocks open up randomly in the desert, and no-one can predict when or where one will strike. Sage can sense them whenever they open up, and the team are always on standby so that when one sweeps across the sand, they are ready to drive into it.

WHY DO THEY POSE A THREAT TO EARTH?

They are dangerous because Vandals and The Sark have access to them too; and unless Battle Force 5 lock the zone down, they can drive through the portal and invade Earth!

HOW CAN STORMSHOCKS BE CLOSED?

Stormshocks close when a Battle Zone is locked down. To do this, the team need to find the key in the Battle Zone, and bring it back through the Stormshock to Earth. This seals the Battle Zone and means no-one else can come through the portal.

BATTLE FORCE 5 PROFILE

SAGE

FACT FILE

NAME: SAGE
ROLE: EXPERT ADVISOR TO BATTLE FORCE 5
WEAPONS: ELECTRIC SHOCK BLAST
SKILLS: HUGE KNOWLEDGE OF MULTIVERSE
VEHICLE: THE MOBIAS COMMAND CENTRE

SAGE IS A SENTIENT – ONE OF AN ANCIENT RACE OF PEOPLE WHO WERE SCATTERED ROUND THE MULTIVERSE WHEN VANDALS AND THE SARK INVADED THEIR TWIN HOME PLANETS. HER HOME PLANET IS THE BLUE SENTIENT PLANET.

THE SENTIENTS BUILT THE MULTIVERSE, INCLUDING ALL OF THE BATTLE ZONES, MANY YEARS AGO. SO SAGE HAS AN UNRIVALLED KNOWLEDGE OF BATTLE ZONES, STORMSHOCKS AND ALL OTHER ASPECTS OF THE MULTIVERSE.

SAGE RELIES ON POWER FROM THE MOBIAS COMMAND CENTRE TO SURVIVE, AND CAN'T BE AWAY FROM IT FOR TOO LONG OR SHE GROWS WEAK.

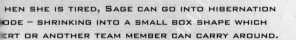

...HEN SHE IS TIRED, SAGE CAN GO INTO HIBERNATION
...ODE – SHRINKING INTO A SMALL BOX SHAPE WHICH
...ERT OR ANOTHER TEAM MEMBER CAN CARRY AROUND.

SAGE CAN'T PASS THROUGH
STORMSHOCKS WITHOUT BEING
WEAKENED, AND ERASING PART
OF HER MEMORY. SO SHE WILL
ONLY TRAVEL THROUGH ONE IN
AN EMERGENCY.

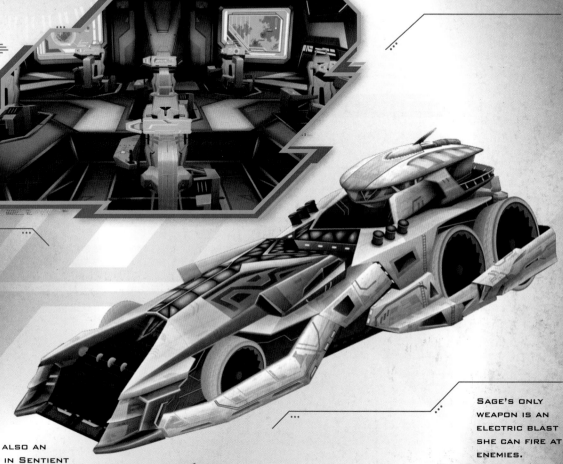

...HE IS ALSO AN
...XPERT IN SENTIENT
...ECHNOLOGY. SHE BUILT
...HE HUB, MADE ALL OF
...HE TEAM'S VEHICLES
...ND SUITS, AND KNOWS
...VERYTHING ABOUT
...HE MOBIAS.

SAGE'S ONLY
WEAPON IS AN
ELECTRIC BLAST
SHE CAN FIRE AT
ENEMIES.

THE SENTIENTS

THE SENTIENTS ARE AN ANCIENT RACE, WHO KNOW
FIRST HAND THE DAMAGE VANDALS AND THE SARK
CAN CAUSE. THEY WERE DRIVEN OFF THEIR TWIN HOME
PLANETS, WHEN ONE WAS INVADED BY EACH OF THE
EVIL ARMIES. THAT'S WHY SAGE IS SO DESPERATE TO
SAVE THE EARTH FROM THE SAME FATE!

PREVIOUS MISSIONS

The adventures of Battle Force 5 so far!

STARTING LINE

Vert goes out for a spin in his racing car, but gets more than he bargained for when he is swept up in a mysterious Stormshock and deposited in a fearsome Battle Zone! When he rescues Sage, she transforms his car for him, and finds him a team to help him save the Earth from the Vandals and Sark. . .

GEARING UP

The team set out on their first mission as a group when a Stormshock opens up in the desert. In the raging battle that follows, Sage is kidnapped – but rescued thanks to some fancy driving by Vert. The team also rescue a Mobias Command Centre and bring it back to The Hub.

COMMON COLD WAR

Hot-headed Agura starts to get annoyed by her team-mates' habits, especially Spinner and his irrational fear of germs! When Zemerik manages to seize control of the Tangler, she nearly blows her top – but some team-work means that Battle Force 5 live to fight another day.

BASIC TRAINING

THE TEAM DECIDE TO GO AND
TRAIN IN AN ALREADY-SECURE
BATTLE ZONE. WHILE THEY ARE
PRACTISING SOME TOP-SPEED
BATTLE MOVES, THEY STUMBLE
ACROSS A SARK FACTORY,
WHICH IS MAKING ZURKS FOR
A NEW ARMY. OF COURSE, THE
TEAM CAN'T JUST LEAVE IT BE,
AND A FIERCE BATTLE IS THE
ONLY SOLUTION!

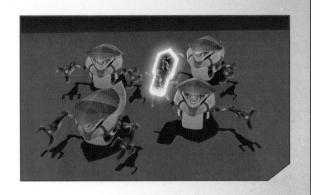

MISSING IN ACTION

TEAM SCOUT ZOOM IS IN A SULK:
HE DOESN'T THINK THAT THE REST
OF THE TEAM APPRECIATE HIS
MARTIAL ARTS SKILLS AND QUICK
THINKING. AS HE GETS MORE
ANNOYED, THOUGH, HE LETS HIS
GUARD DOWN – AND THE VANDALS
POUNCE, CAPTURING HIM. THE
REST OF BATTLE FORCE 5 SOON
REALISE HOW SKILFUL ZOOM IS
WHEN HE TURNS HIS ANGER ON
THE VANDALS AND ESCAPES.

JUNKYARD DOGGED

THE TEAM NEED TO GET THEIR
HANDS ON A BATTLE KEY, BUT
IT IS FLOATING IN A HUGE AND
DANGEROUS JUNK ZONE, AND
GUARDED BY A SAVAGE ROBOT
DOG. FIGHTING FOR SURVIVAL,
SPINNER AND SHERMAN FORM
AN UNLIKELY PACT WITH KALUS
IN ORDER TO MAKE IT BACK HOME.

BEHIND ENEMY LINES

VERT GETS A TASTE OF WHAT IT
IS LIKE TO BE HUNTED, WHEN
HE GETS STRANDED DURING AN
UNDERCOVER MISSION TO PLANET
VANDAL. KALUS CAN'T BELIEVE
HIS LUCK — A REAL, LIVE HUMAN
TO HUNT! AND VERT NEEDS ALL
OF HIS SPEED AND CUNNING
TO KEEP OUT OF THE VANDAL
LEADER'S CLAWS. . .

MY MAN ZUG

STANFORD HAS ALWAYS HAD
A TASTE FOR THE HIGH LIFE
(DID YOU KNOW HE IS DESCENDED
FROM ROYALTY?), BUT THERE'S
SOMETHING SHIFTY ABOUT HIS
NEW SERVANT. IT TURNS OUT
TO BE ZUG, REPROGRAMMED
BY ZEMERIK TO SPY ON
BATTLE FORCE 5!

FRENEMY

IT SEEMS THAT STANFORD
DOES HAVE SOME IMPORTANT
ANCESTORS — HE IS DESCENDED
FROM A FAMOUS EXPLORER AND
RULER OF THE MULTIVERSE. AFTER
DISCOVERING THIS, STANFORD
DECIDES THAT HE SHOULD BE
LEADER OF BATTLE FORCE 5 —
BUT HIS PEACE TREATY WITH THE
VANDALS DOESN'T GO ACCORDING
TO PLAN.

MAN DOWN

During a fierce Battle Zone fight, Zoom is injured by Hatch. He needs an antidote to the poison fast, and the rest of the team have a real challenge as they race to Planet Vandal to find it for him. The clock is ticking. . .

ARTIFICIAL INTELLIGENCE

Diner owner Zeke becomes super-intelligent when a Sentient Data Log is downloaded into his brain. He joins the team in a secret Battle Zone, in a hunt for sentient survivors. And of course, the Sark want a piece of the action too!

DOUBLE DOWN

Strange solar flares are making the Multiverse behave weirdly, and the team can't believe it when they find themselves fighting themselves. . . in the form of an EVIL Battle Force 5! Only the presence of a parallel GOOD Kalus can make things even stranger.

BATTLE FORCE 5 GLOSSARY

Understand everything in the Multiverse!

BATTLE KEY
Powerful device that can open or lock down a Battle Zone.

BATTLE ZONE
Inter-dimensional world specially created for doing battle in.

BLADOR'S QUEST
Sherman's favourite Sci-Fi TV show.

BLUE SENTIENT
Sentients are half-computerised, very intelligent life forms scattered round the Multiverse due to their home planets being invaded. Blue ones are calm and peaceful.

ECHO-MAP
A Map of a Battle Zone produced by analysing sound waves bouncing off objects.

ELECTRO-WHIP
Zemerik's weapon of choice.

ENERGY LEECHES
These creatures can drain the energy out of Battle Force 5 vehicles and technology. Very dangerous.

GERMS
Cybernetic, tiny bacteria that can be dangerous.

HADRON
The energy that drives all Sentient technology, as well as the Sentients themselves.

HANDLER CORNERS
The small town in the desert where Vert lives.

HIBERNATION MODE
Sage can sleep in a tiny box form when she is feeling weak.

HUB
The underground, hi-tech base beneath Vert's garage.

KRYPT ZONE
An inter-dimensional prison from which it is impossible to escape.

MECHA-WASPS
Robotic creatures that go crazy when they hear the sonic blasts from the Reverb.

MINI-ZURKS
Small Zurks that can propel themselves around on wheels.

MOBIAS COMMAND CENTRE

Sentient vehicle that can sustain Sage's life, as well as fixing Battle Force 5 vehicles and providing other hi-tech support.

MODULON 5

Blue Sentient's main city before they were invaded by Vandals.

MULTIVERSE

The inter-dimensional worlds created by the Sentients many years ago.

PORTAL

An entry and exit point from a Battle Zone into another world, e.g. Earth.

RED SENTIENT

Red Sentients are more violent and destructive than Blue ones.

SAGE

Young Blue Sentient who acts as advisor to the team.

SARK

Evil robot warriors who invade other planets.

SHOCKSUIT

Protective race suits made with Sentient technology. Almost indestructible.

STORMSHOCK

Fierce storm that opens up as a portal to a Battle Zone.

VANDAL

Fierce animal hunter-warrior race who want to invade Earth.

ZEKE'S DINER

Battle Force 5's favourite hang-out.

ZURK

Sark foot soldier, with no free will of its own.

MEGA BATTLE FORCE 5 QUIZ

TEST YOUR BF5 KNOWLEDGE WITH THIS TRICKY TEST!

1. WHY IS THE TEAM CALLED BATTLE FORCE 5, WHEN IT HAS 6 PEOPLE IN IT?
A) BECAUSE THERE WERE ORIGINALLY 5 OF THEM
B) BECAUSE THERE ARE 5 VEHICLES
C) NOBODY KNOWS

2. NAME THE LEADER OF THE SARK
A) ZEMERIK
B) ZEMEROD
C) ZURK

3. WHAT IS ZOOM'S MOTORBIKE CALLED?
A) THE RIPPER
B) THE CHANGER
C) THE CHOPPER

4. WHY IS THE REVERB SUITED TO STANFORD'S PERSONALITY?
A) BECAUSE HE LOVES MUSIC
B) BECAUSE HE IS SO TOUGH
C) BECAUSE HE LOVES BIG WHEELS

5. WHAT IS VERT'S SAYING AS HE CHARGES INTO BATTLE?
A) LET'S GO, TEAM!
B) GET READY TO CRASH AND BASH!
C) FOLLOW ME!

6. WHAT IS THIS CHARACTER CALLED?
A) SMURK
B) HITCH
C) HATCH

7. WHAT DOES A STORMSHOCK LOOK LIKE?
A) A GIANT TORNADO
B) A BIG LAKE
C) A DOORWAY

8.   WHICH SENTIENT PLANET DOES SAGE COME FROM?
A)   The Blue Sentient Planet
B)   The Red Sentient Planet
C)   Neither, she comes from Earth

9.   WHICH CHARACTER IS THIS A DETAIL FROM?
A)   Zemerik
B)   Zoom
C)   Agura

10.   WHO IS ZEMERIK'S SECOND-IN-COMMAND?
A)   Zug
B)   Zig
C)   Zag

11.   WHAT IS AGURA'S MAIN HOBBY?
A)   Off-Road Racing
B)   Boxing
C)   Stamp collecting

12.   WHAT IS THIS PICTURE OF?
A)   A Battle Key
B)   A Stormshock
C)   A Battle Zone

13.   WHICH BROTHER IS THE OLDER ONE?
A)   Sherman
B)   Spinner
C)   They are twins

14.   WHOSE SECRET SYMBOL IS THIS?
A)   Zemerik
B)   Kalus
C)   Vert

15.   NAME KALUS'S SECOND-IN-COMMAND
A)   Lizardus
B)   Krocomodo
C)   Snakerama

16. WHO OWNS THIS CAR?

A) KALUS

B) SEVER

C) KROCOMODO

17. WHERE DOES SAGE GET HER ENERGY?

A) FROM THE MOBIAS

B) FROM BATTLE ZONES

C) FROM STORMSHOCKS

18. WHERE DO THE TEAM HANG OUT BETWEEN ADVENTURES?

A) AT SCHOOL

B) AT ZEKE'S DINER

C) AT STANFORD'S HOUSE

19. WHAT IS VERT'S UNDERGROUND BASE CALLED?

A) THE HUT

B) THE HOUSE

C) THE HUB

20. WHERE DO VANDALS COME FROM?

A) VANDALIUS

B) VANDAL TOWN

C) PLANET VANDAL

21. WHAT DOES TAKING A BATTLE KEY HOME TO EARTH DO?

A) LOCKS DOWN THE BATTLE ZONE

B) OPENS UP A BATTLE ZONE

C) FREEZES A BATTLE ZONE

22. WHICH CAR IS THIS A DETAIL FROM?

A) THE CHOPPER

B) THE TANGLER

C) THE REVERB

23. WHAT ARE BF5'S PROTECTIVE RACE SUITS CALLED?

A) BODY PROTECTORS

B) SHOCKSUITS

C) RACE OUTFITS

24. WHO DRIVES THE SABER?

A) STANFORD
B) KALUS
C) VERT

25. WHO MADE THE MULTIVERSE?

A) THE SENTIENTS
B) THE VANDALS
C) THE SARK

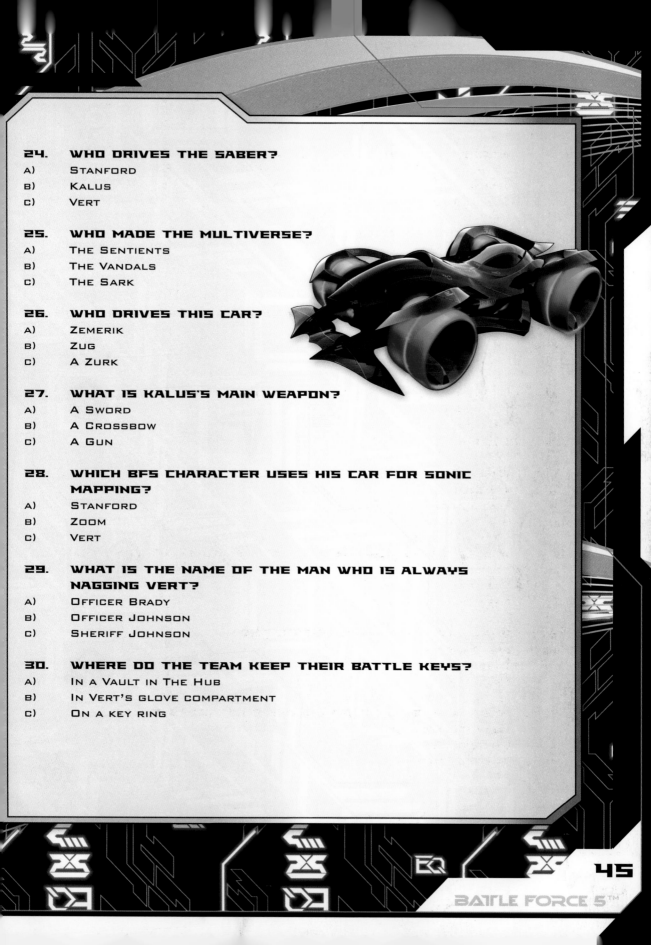

26. WHO DRIVES THIS CAR?

A) ZEMERIK
B) ZUG
C) A ZURK

27. WHAT IS KALUS'S MAIN WEAPON?

A) A SWORD
B) A CROSSBOW
C) A GUN

28. WHICH BF5 CHARACTER USES HIS CAR FOR SONIC MAPPING?

A) STANFORD
B) ZOOM
C) VERT

29. WHAT IS THE NAME OF THE MAN WHO IS ALWAYS NAGGING VERT?

A) OFFICER BRADY
B) OFFICER JOHNSON
C) SHERIFF JOHNSON

30. WHERE DO THE TEAM KEEP THEIR BATTLE KEYS?

A) IN A VAULT IN THE HUB
B) IN VERT'S GLOVE COMPARTMENT
C) ON A KEY RING

BATTLE KEYS

WHAT ARE BATTLE KEYS?

Battle Keys are powerful objects that can open and close portals to Battle Zones. By finding a Battle Key in the Battle Zone and taking it back to Earth, Battle Force 5 can shut down a Battle Zone completely.

WHERE ARE THEY FOUND?

They are often hidden in hard places or inside puzzles in the Battle Zones. Even when they have been found, it isn't always easy to reach them.

Alien City Battle Key

BioMech Battle Key

WHY DO THE VANDALS AND SARK WANT THEM?

So that they can have control over a Battle Zone, and use it to enter Earth and conquer it.

Junkyard Battle Key

Desert Battle Key

MCEscher Battle Key

Gridstone Battle Key

WHAT DO THE TEAM DO WITH THEM?

The team bring them back to Earth, lock down the Battle Zones and store them in a super-safe vault in the Hub. They can go back to the Battle Zones if needed, but no-one else can use them.

BATTLE FORCE 5
CERTIFICATE

THIS IS TO CERTIFY THAT

_____

AGED _____

FROM _____

HAS STUDIED THIS BOOK, AND COMPLETED THE QUIZ,
AND IS THEREFORE READY FOR ACTION AS A
FULL BATTLE FORCE 5 MEMBER!

SIGNED

_____

QUIZ ANSWERS

FIND OUT HOW YOU DID!

1:B;	2:A;	3:C;	4:A;	5:B;	6:C;	7:A;	8:A;	9:C;	10:A;
11:A;	12:B;	13:B;	14:C;	15:B;	16:B;	17:A;	18:B;	19:C;	20:C;
21:A;	22:C;	23:B;	24:C;	25:A;	26:A;	27:B;	28:A;	29:C;	30:A

TOTAL SCORE:

HOW DID YOU DO?

■ 0-10 CORRECT: YOU'VE GOT A LOT TO LEARN ABOUT THE MULTIVERSE. HAVE ANOTHER READ THROUGH THIS BOOK TO BECOME AN EXPERT!

■ 11-20 CORRECT: GOOD BATTLE FORCE 5 KNOWLEDGE. YOU STILL HAVE ROOM FOR MORE FACTS, THOUGH – RE-WATCH YOUR FAVOURITE EPISODES AND REMEMBER ALL THE DETAILS!

■ 21-30: YOU'RE A BATTLE FORCE 5 GENIUS, GOOD ENOUGH TO JOIN THE TEAM ON A DANGEROUS MISSION INSIDE A BATTLE ZONE!